The *Naughty Ann*

Story   by   Beverley   Randell

Illustrated   by   Pat   Reynolds

The **Naughty Ann** was painted blue,
The **Naughty Ann** was clean and new.

*The fishing boat (the **Jolly Jean**) was not so new and not so clean.*

"Go away. You smell of fish.
Go away!" said the *Naughty Ann.*

"No," said the *Jolly Jean.*
"I'm staying here."

"But you smell of fish,"
said the *Naughty Ann.*
"I will not stay here with **you**."

"I'm going out to sea,"
said the *Naughty Ann*,
and away she went.

Out at sea
the wind came up,
and the waves
got bigger and bigger.

"Help!" said the *Naughty Ann*.
"A big green wave is coming!"

"Help!   Help!"
shouted the *Naughty Ann.*
"Who will help me?

Mayday! Mayday!

I'm upside down!"

13

"I'm coming," said the *Jolly Jean.*

"I'm up again," said the *Naughty Ann.*
"But look at me! I'm broken!
 Help! **Mayday**!"

"Here's a rope,"
 said the *Jolly Jean.*

"You **saved** me!"
said the *Naughty Ann*.   "Thanks.
I **like** the smell of fish, now."